NINETIES
Playalong *for* Clarinet

G000107928

WISE PUBLICATIONS
London/New York/Paris/Sydney/Copenhagen/Madrid

Fingering Guide

Transposition

The Bb clarinet sounds a major second below the written pitch.

Rule: Written C sounds Bb

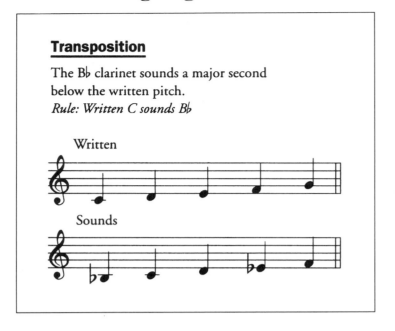

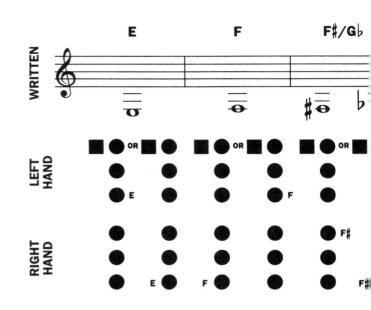

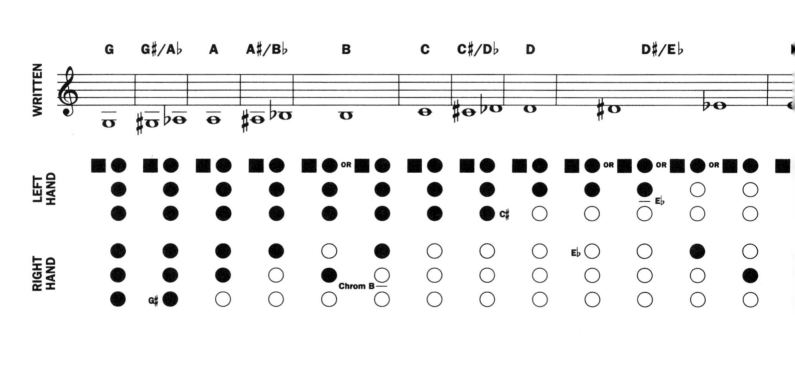

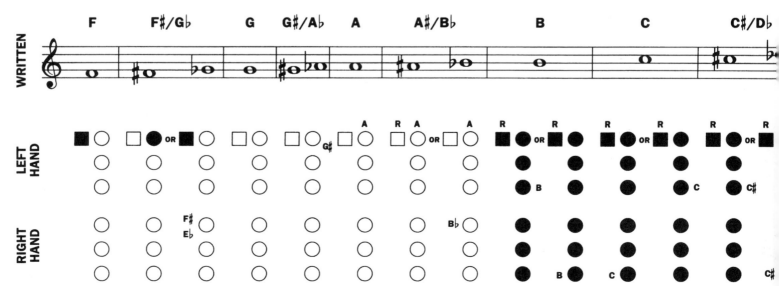

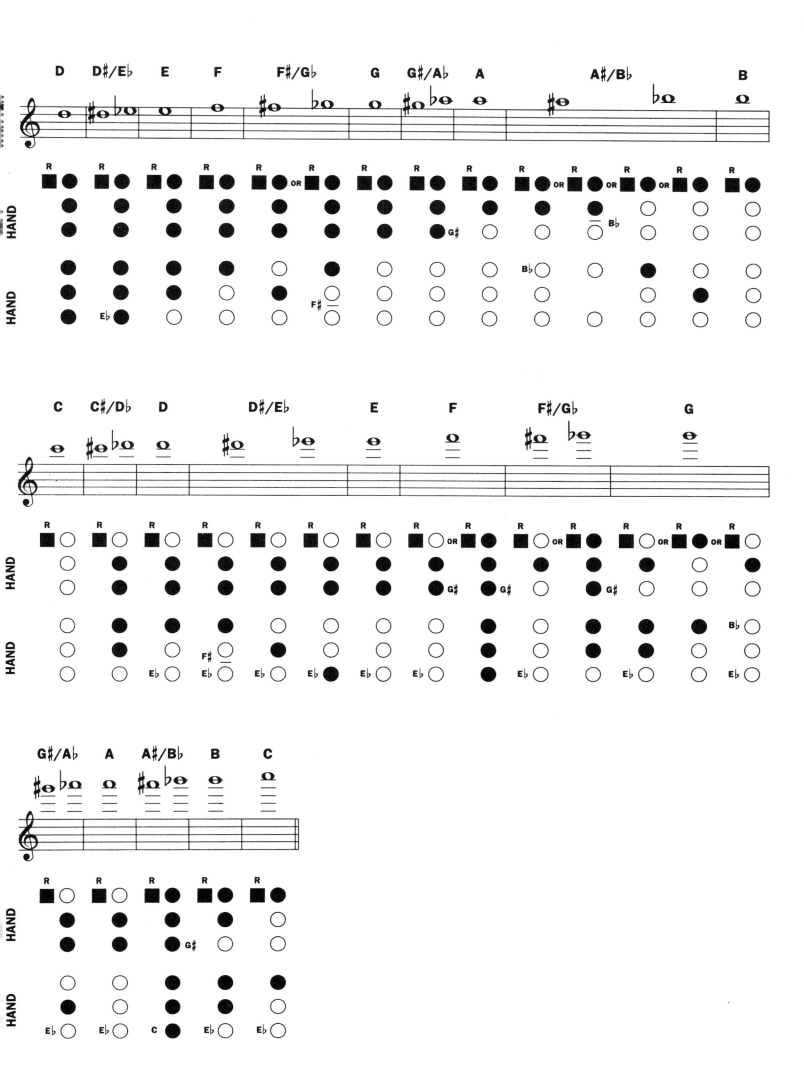

Falling Into You

Words & Music by Rick Nowles, Marie-Claire D'Ubalio & Billy Steinberg

Moderately

(Everything I Do) I Do It For You

Words by Bryan Adams & Robert John 'Mutt' Lange
Music by Michael Kamen

Slow rock

I Am Blessed

Words & Music by Marsha Malamet & Mark Mueller

rall.   Slower

dim.

I Believe I Can Fly

Words & Music by Robert Kelly

Slow but rhythmic

Never Ever

Words & Music by Shaznay Lewis
Music by Rickidy Raw

Slow beat Swung ♪'s

fade on repeat

19

Tears In Heaven

Words & Music by Eric Clapton & Will Jennings

Moderately

2 Become 1

Words & Music by Victoria Aadams, Melanie Brown, Emma Bunton, Melanie Chisholm, Geri Halliwell, Matt Rowe & Richard Stannard

Languidly

Repeat to fade

Torn

Words & Music by Anne Preven, Scott Cutler & Phil Thornalley

Repeat to fade

26

Words

Words & Music by Barry Gibb, Robin Gibb & Maurice Gibb

Moderately

rall.

Without You

Words & Music by Peter Ham & Tom Evans

Slow

mp

f

Repeat to fade

Exclusive Distributors:
Music Sales Limited
8/9 Frith Street, London W1V 5TZ, England.
Music Sales Pty Limited
120 Rothschild Avenue, Rosebery, NSW 2018, Australia.

Order No. AM952853
ISBN 0-7119-7083-1
This book © Copyright 1998 by Wise Publications.

Book design by Michael Bell Design.
Music arranged by Paul Honey.
Music processed by Enigma Music Production Services.
Cover photography by George Taylor.
Printed in the United Kingdom by Page Bros., Norwich, Norfolk.

CD produced by Paul Honey.
Instrumental solos by John Whelan.
Engineered by Kester Sims.

Your Guarantee of Quality:
As publishers, we strive to produce every book to
the highest commercial standards.
The music has been freshly engraved and the book has been
carefully designed to minimise awkward page turns and
to make playing from it a real pleasure.
Particular care has been given to specifying acid-free, neutral-sized
paper made from pulps which have not been elemental chlorine bleached.
This pulp is from farmed sustainable forests and was
produced with special regard for the environment.
Throughout, the printing and binding have been planned to
ensure a sturdy, attractive publication which should give years of enjoyment.
If your copy fails to meet our high standards,
please inform us and we will gladly replace it.

Music Sales' complete catalogue describes thousands of
titles and is available in full colour sections by subject,
direct from Music Sales Limited.
Please state your areas of interest and send a
cheque/postal order for £1.50 for postage to:
Music Sales Limited, Newmarket Road, Bury St. Edmunds, Suffolk IP33 3YB.